Reading for Meaning   THIRD EDITION

Up and Away

PAUL McKEE · M. LUCILE HARRISON

ANNIE McCOWEN · ELIZABETH LEHR

HOUGHTON MIFFLIN COMPANY · **Boston**

NEW YORK · ATLANTA · GENEVA, ILL. · DALLAS · PALO ALTO

What you will find:

HERE AND THERE

FOR YOU

HAPPY DAYS

Here and There

Here come:

What About Willie?

Willie Was Cold

It was cold.

And there was Willie

out in the cold.

Willie was a little kitten.

He did not know where to go.

He wanted a home.

He wanted a bed to sleep in.

But there he was out in the cold

with no home to go to.

And there was Tommy.

He wanted a fish.

He could see the fish in the water,
but he could not get it on his string.

The fish was cold,
but fish like to be cold.

Tommy was cold, too,
but he did not like it at all.

Tommy had a house to go into.

He put down the string
and went into his house.

Tommy and Willie

Tommy wanted a fish.

He wanted a kitten, too.

A little yellow and black kitten.

He could make

black and yellow kittens.

And that is what he did.

Willie was black and yellow, too.

But he was out in the cold.

He did not know about Tommy.

And Tommy did not know
about Willie.

Tommy looked out into the night.
How wet and cold the night was!
The fish was out in the night,
but fish like the wet and the cold.

Tommy looked and looked
at all his black and yellow kittens.
Then he went to bed.

Willie wanted a home.
He looked for one,
but he did not find it.

Willie was cold.

And he was wet, too.

He was as wet as wet can be.

It was a bad night for a kitten
to be out in the cold.

Willie wanted a home.

He wanted a fire to sleep by.

But no one wanted a little black
and yellow kitten.

No one but Tommy.

And Tommy did not know that Willie
wanted a home and a fire to sleep by.

Willie Hears Something

What was that?
Willie could hear something.
Then he could see feet
in the dark night.

Willie went up to the feet.
The feet went into a house.
He went in with the feet to look
for a bed and a fire to sleep by.
No one saw the little wet kitten.
It was too dark to see
a little black and yellow kitten.

11

As soon as Willie was in the house,
he ran as fast as his feet could go.
Up and up he ran.
And there was a bed.
He ran to it and got up on it.
He got up on it with his wet feet.
Soon he was not cold.

He was about to go to sleep.
Then what did Willie hear?
He could hear somebody.

Willie could hear somebody coming.
Somebody was coming to the bed.
Willie was as still as he could be.
But somebody saw him.
She looked at his wet feet.

"See what you did!" she said.
"Get out of my bed!
Get out of this house!"

Willie ran as fast as he could.
Out he went into the dark night.
It was still cold and dark and he
wanted a home and a fire to sleep by.

Willie Finds a House

Willie ran on and on.
Then he came to another house.
It was little, like Willie.

The little house was dark and still.
Willie did not hear a sound.
Willie put his head into the house.
He still did not hear a sound.

Then something went, "Woof! WOOF!"
Out jumped Willie!
And out jumped a big dog!
Willie ran as fast as he could go.
The big dog did not get him.

Willie was still out in the dark.
He ran on and on all night.
He was as wet and as cold
as a kitten could be.

As soon as night was gone,
Willie looked around for somebody.
Then he saw a little yellow house.
So he ran all around it and asked
somebody to come and let him in.
But no one came.
Tommy was in the yellow house,
but he did not hear a sound.

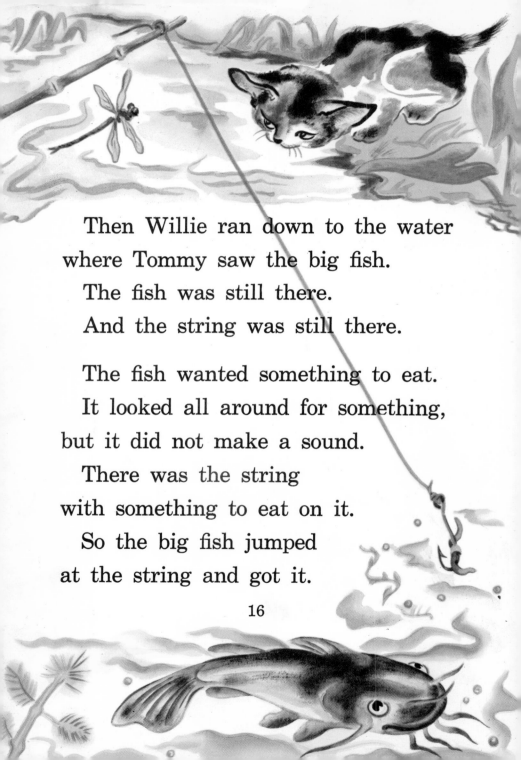

Then Willie ran down to the water
where Tommy saw the big fish.
The fish was still there.
And the string was still there.

The fish wanted something to eat.
It looked all around for something,
but it did not make a sound.
There was the string
with something to eat on it.
So the big fish jumped
at the string and got it.

16

Willie and the Fish

Willie saw the string jump.

He ran and jumped on it
with all his feet.

Then he pulled on the string.

The fish did not like that.

He saw that Willie had the string.

Willie could eat a fish.

So the big fish pulled and pulled.

Willie did not want to eat the fish.

Willie wanted to play.

So he pulled and pulled, and soon
the string was all around his feet.

The string was all around Willie.

He could not get away.

The fish was on the string.

So it could not get away.

The fish pulled hard.

Willie pulled hard, too.

Then the fish pulled so hard

that it pulled Willie into the water.

It pulled his feet into the water.

It pulled all of Willie

into the water — all but his head.

"It will EAT ME!" cried Willie.

The fish still pulled very hard.
Willie cried and cried for help.
He wanted somebody to hear him.
He cried so hard that somebody
did hear him.

"That sounds like a little kitten,"
said Tommy.
Tommy looked out of his house
and saw Willie in the water.
He ran very fast to help Willie.

"I am coming!" cried Tommy.

Tommy got hold of the string.
He pulled very hard.
The fish pulled hard, too.

And Willie pulled away from Tommy.
He did not know
that Tommy had come to help him.

Then Tommy pulled very, very hard.
Down he went, but out came Willie.
And out came the big fish
that Tommy had wanted to eat.

Tommy Gets a Kitten

So Tommy got what he wanted.
He got a yellow and black kitten
and the big fish, too.

And what about Willie?
Willie got a very good home
and a bed and a fire to sleep by.

Jack Rabbit and the Hiccups

Jack Rabbit had the hiccups.
He wanted to eat but he could not.
The hiccups got in his way.

Can Red Calf Help?

"You sound funny!" said Red Calf.
Then he laughed and laughed at Jack.

"Hiccups are not funny," said Jack.
"How can I make them go away?"

"Mother had hiccups," said Red Calf.
"She ran around and laughed."

23

So Jack ran around and around
and laughed and laughed.
But he still had the hiccups,
and Red Calf still laughed at him.

"Daddy had hiccups," said Red Calf.
"He stood on his head.
If you can do that, it may help."

So Jack Rabbit stood on his head,
but that did not help at all.

"This is bad," he said.
And he went on his way.

Mr. Zebra Wants to Help

Mr. Zebra saw Jack coming.
"I hear you have hiccups," he said.
"Hiccups are very, very bad,
if you do not do something for them."

"Mr. Zebra, I did what Red Calf
wanted me to do," said Jack.
"I ran around and around
and I laughed and laughed.
I stood on my head, too.
But my hiccups did not go away."

"You stood on your head?"
said Mr. Zebra, and then he laughed.
"Tricks like that are no good.
Do you know what I do
if I have the hiccups?"

"No, Mr. Zebra," said Jack.
"What do you do for hiccups?"

"I count my stripes," said Mr. Zebra.
"Jump up on my back.
You may count my stripes
if you know how to count."

"I can count to three," said Jack.
He jumped up on the back
of Mr. Zebra to count his stripes.
"One, two, three," he said.

Then Jack Rabbit jumped down.
He stood very still
to see if the hiccups had gone away.
No, he still had them.

"Mr. Zebra, it will never help me
to count your stripes!" Jack cried.

And he went on his way.

Mrs. Ostrich Wants to Help

Mrs. Ostrich saw Jack coming.

"Hiccups?" she asked.

"You could do something for them if you wanted to."

"I did, Mrs. Ostrich," said Jack.

"I laughed and I ran around.

I stood on my head.

Mr. Zebra had me count his stripes.

I can count to three, Mrs. Ostrich.

The hiccups never did go away."

"Count three," said Mrs. Ostrich.
"Then put your head into the sand.
My hiccups go away when I do that."

So Jack said, "One, two, three."
He put his head into the sand.
Then he stood up to see
if he still had the hiccups.

"Mrs. Ostrich, sand will never
make my hiccups go away," said Jack.

"This will never do," he said,
as he went on his way.

Can the Kangaroos Help?

Jack Rabbit was not happy.
He went to see Little Kangaroo.

"Little Kangaroo, what do you do
for hiccups?" Jack asked.
"I laughed and I ran around.
I stood on my head.
Mr. Zebra had me count his stripes.
I put my head into the sand.
Mrs. Ostrich does that for hiccups.
When I stood up, I still had them."

"Hiccups?" asked Little Kangaroo.
He sat down and looked at Jack.
"When I have hiccups, Mother puts me
into her pocket and jumps around."

"My mother has no pocket," said Jack.

Little Kangaroo said to his mother,
"Jack Rabbit has the hiccups.
Will you jump around with him
if he gets into your pocket?"

"I will be happy to do that
for Jack," said Mrs. Kangaroo.

It was a very hot day.

But Mrs. Kangaroo jumped around very fast with Jack in her pocket.

She wanted to make Jack happy.

When she sat down, Jack jumped out of her pocket and sat down, too.

"My! This is a hot day!" he said.

"How about the hiccups?" she asked.

"I still have them," said Jack.

"Mrs. Kangaroo, this will never do!"

And he went on his way.

32

The day was hot and so was Jack.

"I ran around and laughed," he said.
"I stood on my head.
Mr. Zebra had me count his stripes.
I put my head into the sand
because Mrs. Ostrich said to.
Mrs. Kangaroo jumped with me
in her pocket.
That pocket was very hot,
and I still have the hiccups.
This will never, never do!"

Jack Rabbit was not happy.
He sat down and cried big tears.

White Horse Has Hiccups

Jack Rabbit cried big tears
because he was not happy.

Up came White Horse.
He said, "Jack, I have hiccups.
Do you know what to do for them?"

"I know what not to do," said Jack.
"Do not count stripes on Mr. Zebra!
Do not put your head into the sand
because Mrs. Ostrich asks you to!
And do not let Mrs. Kangaroo
put you into her pocket on a hot day."

Jack sat still and cried big tears
because he was not happy.

"What can we do?" asked White Horse.

"Ask those three pigs," said Jack.

The three pigs were happy.
They were in the water
because it was a hot day.
They sat in water on hot days.

White Horse said to the pigs,
"Jack and I have the hiccups.
What do you do for hiccups?"

The pigs were still in the water
and they were very, very happy.

"We never have hiccups," said one.
"But Mother had them one day."

"What did she do?" asked the horse.

"She sat on ice," said another pig.

"Ice! Ice!" cried White Horse.
"Where can we find ice
on a hot day like this?"

"We do not know," said the pigs.

Then White Horse cried big tears
because the pigs were no help.

"What do the pigs do?" asked Jack
when White Horse came back.

"They said that Mrs. Pig sat on ice
for her hiccups," said White Horse.
"The pigs were no help."

Jack still sat and cried.
"That will never do," he said.
"No one could find ice on a hot day.
I will get a little water.
Then I will go to sleep."

"I will go home," said White Horse.

What Did Help?

When Jack had had a good sleep,
he got up and stood very still.
He wanted to see
if the hiccups had gone away.
He could not hear a sound.
He jumped around and around.
Then he stood very still.
The hiccups were gone!

But Jack Rabbit never did find out
what makes hiccups go away.

A Way to Make New Words

Up is a word that you know.

Put **c** with **up**.

Now you have a new word, **cup**.

Put **p** with **in**.

What new word will that make?

Put **h** with **at**.

What new word will you have?

Put **w** with **all**.

Now what word do you have?

Put **s** with **it**.

What new word will that make?

Put **l** with **and**.

What new word will you have?

Put **sh** with **out**.

What new word does that make?

You hear the sound of **r**
in **rabbit, run,** and **ran.**

Take **sh** out of **show.**
Put in **r** and you have **row.**

Here is a row of dogs.

Hear the sound of **sh**
in **show** and **she.**

Take **T** away from **Tip.**
Put in **sh** and you have **ship.**

Where could you see a ship?

You can hear the sound of **wh**
in **what, when,** and **white.**

Take **m** away from **my.**
Put in **wh** and you have **why.**

Why did Jack Rabbit want help?

The Little Calf Who Cried

Who Was Happy?

Mr. Black was very happy.

We know he was happy.

One day a big box came down
on his head.

That was no fun at all for him.

But still he was very happy.

Mrs. Black was happy, too.
We know she was happy.
One day her feet went up
and she sat down in the water.
She got very wet,
but still she was happy.

Mr. Black had a happy horse.
We know he was happy.
See what somebody did to him?
That was no fun for him.
Still he was happy.

Mrs. Black had three happy pigs.
We know her pigs were happy.
They looked for something to eat.
They could not find it.
Still the three pigs were happy.

Who Was Not Happy?

Mr. and Mrs. Black had
a little calf.

That little calf was never happy.

When the days were hot, he cried
because he was too hot.

When the days were wet, he cried
because he was too wet.

When it was dark, he cried
because it was too dark.

He was never, never happy.

He cried all day and all night.

In the Ice

One day it was very, very cold.
That day the little calf cried.
He cried because it was too cold.
He sat down and cried big tears.
The tears ran down all around him.
There he sat in his tears.
The day was so cold
that soon the tears were ice.

When the little calf wanted
to get up, he could not do it.
He could not get out of the ice.
So he cried about that.

Mr. Black went to help.
But what he did was no good.
He could not get the calf out.

Mrs. Black went to help.
She put hot water on the ice.
That did no good.

The horse went to help.
He pulled on the calf.
But that did no good at all.

No one could get the calf
out of the ice.

"This is bad!" said Mr. Black.
"We will never get him out."

Mr. Black stood and looked
at the little calf.

Then he sat down and cried.

He cried very, very hard.

"This is bad!" said Mrs. Black.
And she sat down and cried, too.

The pigs cried big tears.
The horse cried big tears.
They all sat down and cried
because the calf was still in the ice.

Out of the Ice

The little calf looked at them.

When he saw how funny they looked,
he laughed.

He laughed very hard.

He laughed and laughed.

He laughed so hard
that his feet went up and down.

His head went up and down.

All of him went up and down.

And out of the ice he came.

After that the little calf was happy.
He never cried when the days were hot.
He never cried when the days were wet.
He never cried when it was dark.
He never cried when it was cold.

But for days the little calf
cried when he sat down.

52

For You

Look for:

The Boat Ride

The New Boat

The Tooseys had a new boat.
They had never had a ride in it.
There were Mrs. Toosey
and five big and little Tooseys.

56

First came Willie and Tommy Toosey.
They were big boys.
Then came Jack and Dick Toosey.
They were little boys.
After them came Dot and Mrs. Toosey.

"It will take a big boat to hold me
and five of you," said Mrs. Toosey.

Willie was first to see the boat.
"It is green and orange!" he cried.
And away ran the five little Tooseys.

Tommy was first to get to the boat.
"We can not ride in this," he cried.
"It has water in it."

"Find the cans you had when you came
to fish," said Mrs. Toosey.
"Take the water out with them."

"They are not here now," said Tommy.

"If we all help, we can tip the boat and let the water out," said Willie.

"Then we can ride in the boat."

"Before you get into the boat, put on these caps," said Mrs. Toosey.

"Come here and put them on before you get away from me.

Then I can see if all five of you come back.

Tommy gets the first cap, a red one.

Dot gets orange and Jack gets green."

"Yellow for Dick," said Mrs. Toosey.
"Blue for Willie and violet for me.
Now before you go, let me see
if all the caps are here.

Red cap, orange cap, yellow cap,
green cap, blue cap, violet cap.

Yes, they are all here.

Now if all the caps come back,
I will know all of you are here."

First they put on the caps.
Then they ran to the boat.

Tip the Boat

"I will count to five," said Tommy.

"When I say 'Five,' tip the boat.

One, two, three, four, —

No! No! Not before I say 'Five.'

Now all of you count with me to five.

One, two, three, four, five!

Tip the boat!"

They could not do it.

"Red, orange, yellow, green,

blue, violet," said Mrs. Toosey.

"I will say them and say them."

"Mother!" cried Tommy.
"Help us tip the boat over!"

Mrs. Toosey came to help.

"I will count to five again,"
said Tommy.
"When I say 'Five,' tip it over.
One, two, three, four, five.
Over! Over! Over!"

But the boat did not go over.
It came down again on the water.
It came down hard, as it did before.
All the Tooseys got very wet.

A Wet Ride

"That was bad!" said Tommy.

"I say so, too," said Mrs. Toosey.
"We may never ride in our boat,
but we will not do that over again!"

"We can ride in our boat
with the water in it," said Willie.
"We are all as wet as can be now."

"May we, Mother?" they all cried.

"Yes! — But it has to be
a little ride," said Mrs. Toosey.

"This is fun!" cried Dot.

"May we put water into our boat before we ride in it again?"

"Mother! Mother!" cried Tommy. "The water is coming up in the boat. Our boat will go down with us!"

"Look, Tommy!" cried Mrs. Toosey. "That thing down there is to let the water out of our boat. Get that thing out."

"What thing?" asked Dick,
and all the little Tooseys stood up.

"This thing!" cried Tommy.
He pulled hard, and out it came.

But the water did not run out.
It began coming in very fast
and the boat began to go down.

"Jump! Jump!" cried Mrs. Toosey.
"Jump before we all go down!"
So into the water they all jumped.

Down they went,
but up they came again.

Then they all ran for the sand.

Mrs. Toosey got there first.

When they were all on the sand,
she began to say:

"Red, orange, yellow, green, blue —
No violet cap!

Red, orange, yellow, green, blue —
Where is our violet cap?

One of us is gone!"

Who Is Gone?

"Here is Willie," said Tommy.
"And here are Jack and Dick.
There is Dot, and here I am.
We are all here!"

Willie began to count,
"One, two, three, four, five.
Here are four boys and one girl.
That makes five of us."

"No violet cap!" cried Mrs. Toosey,
and she went into the water again.

"No violet cap!" cried Mrs. Toosey.
"I can not find the violet cap!"
She began to look around again.

"It is on your head!" cried Dick.

Mrs. Toosey came back.
"So it is!" she said.
"What do you know about that!
What a funny thing that is!"
And she laughed and laughed.

"But our boat is gone," cried Dot
"We can never ride in it again "

Mr. Toosey Helps

Then up came Mr. Toosey.
There the Tooseys stood on the sand.
"What is this all about?" he asked.

"Our boat went down," said Tommy.

"We can get it," said Mr. Toosey.
"I can still see it out there.
Come on and help me!"

Soon the boat was back on the sand,
and all the water was out of it.

"Here is our boat as good
as it was before!" said Dick.

"Look at this!" said Mr. Toosey.
"Put this thing back into the boat
and never take it out again."

"We know!" said Tommy.

"Come on!" cried Mrs. Toosey.
"Get in and we will go for a ride!
But first, put on your caps."

70

Mrs. Toosey began again —
"Red, orange, yellow,
green, blue, violet.
Red, orange, yellow,
green, blue, violet."
And away they all went
in the green and orange boat.

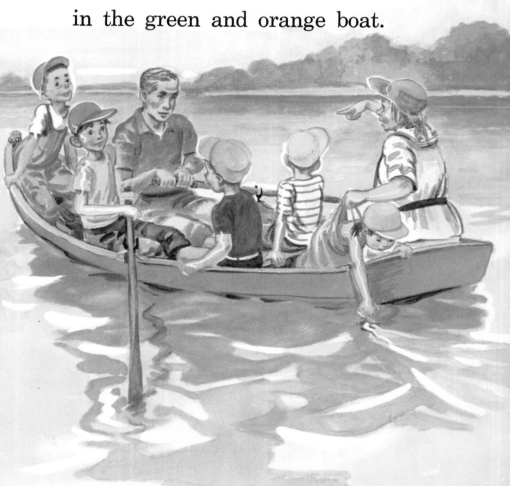

P Is for Paints

Who Gets the Paints?

"Janet, see the paints and pencils that Daddy got for us," said Jack.

Janet went to look at them.
"Are the paints for me?" she asked.

"No, the paints are mine," said Jack.
"The pencils are for you, Janet.
When you get to be as big as I am,
you will get paints, too."

Janet said to herself,
"I want paints now."

Janet wanted the paints.

"I will see if I can find a way
to get them," she said to herself.

When Jack began to paint a picture,
Janet went to look at it.

"Those paints make your picture
look funny," she said.

"You could make a good picture
with these pencils.

See all the colors there are!

I will let you have the pencils.

I will take the paints."

Jack looked at the pencils.
"No, thank you, Janet," he said.
"I want to paint my pictures."

"But just look at these pencils,"
said Janet.
"See how many colors there are!"

"I have just as many colors
in my paint box," said Jack.

Janet said to herself,
"I do not want these pencils.
What can I do to get those paints?"

Soon Janet came back with a toy pig.
"Jack will like this toy pig,"
she said to herself.
"He can put his money into it."

"Jack, here is a toy pig
to put your money into," she said.
"Just look at the pictures on it!
See how many colors are in them!
I will give you this toy pig
and all my pencils for your paints."

"I have no money," said Jack.
"What do I want with a toy pig?
I want to paint pictures."

Still Janet did not give up.
"I will have to get some money
for Jack," she said to herself.

Soon she came back with it.
"Jack, here is some money
to put into the toy pig," she said.
"Now you will have some money,
a toy pig, and all these pencils.
Just see how many things
you will get for your paints!"

Jack laughed and said,
"Take your things and go away.
I want to paint pictures."

Janet went to her mother and said, "Mother, I want to paint pictures.

How can I get some paints?

Jack will not let me have his.

I asked him for them just now.

I wanted him to take my pencils.

I wanted to give him my toy pig and some money to put into it, too.

He just laughed at me."

"Maybe you can still find a way to get some paints," said her mother.

Prizes for the Party

Just then Janet saw Dot.
Dot was on her way home.
Janet ran out to see her.

"Janet, see what I have!" cried Dot.
"Here are some prizes for my party.
Maybe you will get the first prize."

"Maybe I will," said Janet.

Then she said to herself,
"Maybe there are paints in one box.
Maybe I will get them for a prize."

Janet ran back into the house.
"Mother, maybe I will get
some paints after all," she said.

"How?" asked her mother.

"I saw Dot just now," said Janet.
"She had four prizes for her party.
Maybe one prize is paints.
Maybe I can win that prize.
I can run fast.
If there is a race, I can win it."

"Maybe you can," said her mother.

When Janet got to the party,
she saw the four prizes.

One box had a big *A* on it.
One had *B* on it, and one had *M*.
Another had a big *P* on it.

Janet said to herself,
"*A* may be for airplane.
Maybe *M* is for money
and *B* for ball.
P could be for paints.
I want to win that prize.
I will run fast and win a race."

Races and Prizes

Soon all the boys and girls
were at the party and the fun began.

"A peanut race is first," said Dot.

Janet said to herself,
"Maybe I can win the peanut race.
I will not take the airplane.
I will take the box with *P* on it."

Soon the peanut race was over.
Janet got three peanuts,
but Bill White got four peanuts.

"Bill wins first prize," said Dot.

"Now we will put the head
on the zebra," said Dot.

"That is not hard to do,"
Janet said to herself.
"I did not win the peanut race,
but I can win this and get a prize.
Bill White will choose first,
and he will choose the airplane.
Then I will choose,
and I will take the paints."

But Janet did not win.
May Black did.

"Now for the bag race!" said Dot.
"Choose a bag and get into it.
I will count to three.
Then hop or jump to me."

Janet got into a big bag.
"One, two, three – go!" cried Dot.

They all began to hop or jump.
Janet jumped just a little way.
Then down she went in the bag.

"Tommy Green wins the bag race!"
cried Dot.

"Get out of your bags," said Dot.
"Now we will jump rope."

Janet said, "I have to win now
or I will not get a prize.
I will jump rope as fast as I can."

Janet could jump rope very fast.
She did win that prize.

"Now I will get to choose a prize,"
she said to herself.
"But Bill White will choose first.
Then May and Tommy will choose.
I may not get the prize I want."

After they had jumped rope,
they went into the house and sat down.
Dot gave them party caps to put on.
Her mother gave them some ice cream.
Then she came in with a big cake.

"A birthday cake!" cried a boy.
"This is a good party!
We have ice cream and cake too!"
Then Dot gave them bags of peanuts
to take home from the party.

Which Prize Will It Be?

The ice cream and cake went fast.
Then Dot came with the four prizes.

She said, "Bill will choose first.
He was first in the peanut race.
Which box do you choose, Bill?
Which will it be?
A, or *B*, or *M*, or *P*?"

"Not box *P*, Bill! Not box *P*!"
Janet said to herself.

Bill looked and looked and looked.
Then he said, "I choose the box
with *B* on it, because *B* is for Bill."

"Now May will choose," said Dot.
"Which do you want, May?
Which do you say?
The box with *M* or *P* or *A*?"

May looked at the box with *A* on it.
She looked at the box with *M*.
Then she looked and looked at box *P*.

"Not that one, May! Not that one!"
Janet said to herself.

Then May looked again at box *M*.
"I choose this box with *M* on it,
because *M* is for May," she said.

"Tommy will choose now," said Dot.
"Which will you have, Tommy?
Which of the two?
One is for Janet, and one is for you."

Tommy looked and looked at box *A*.
Then he looked and looked at box *P*.

"Take *A*, Tommy! Take *A*! Take *A*!"
Janet said over and over to herself.

But Tommy said, "I choose box *P*."

"Box *A* is yours, Janet," said Dot.

"Thank you, Dot," said Janet.

"Show us your prizes," said Dot.
"Bill, show your prize first."

Bill White said, "*B* is for boat.
I got it for the peanut race."

May Black said, "*M* is for money.
I got some toy money to play with."

Tommy Green said, "*P* is for paints.
I got these for the bag race."

"*A* is for airplane," said Janet.
"I jumped rope for this airplane."

How It All Came Out

Janet got home
and put the airplane away.
Soon Jack came in.
"Was it a good party?" he asked.

"We had ice cream," she said.
"I had a big dish of ice cream,
some cake, and a bag of peanuts."

"Were there many prizes?" he asked.

"Four," said Janet.
"Tommy got a box of paints.
I got a toy airplane."

"A toy airplane?" Jack asked.
"What color is it?"

"Orange," said Janet.
Soon she came back with it.

"Just what I want!" said Jack.
"What will you take for it?"

"Your paints," said Janet.

"Here they are," said Jack.
"Give me the airplane."

"That was a good party," said Janet,
as she went away with her paints.

Say the words **white** and **kite**.

Take the **k** away from **kite**.

Put in **b** and you have **bite**.

Can you take a bite of cake?

Give me a bite of your cake.

Say the words **Bill, will,** and **still**.

Take the **w** away from **will**.

Put in **h** and you have **hill**.

Who went up the hill?

How did they come down the hill?

Say the words **big** and **pig**.

Take the **b** away from **big**.

Put in **d** and you have **dig**.

Where do you like to dig?

With what do you dig?

Take l away from **let.**
Put in **p** and you have **pet.**
Put in **m** and you have **met.**

One day I let my pet get away.
When I met the pet, it was all wet.

Take **wh** from **when.**
Put in **p** and you have **pen.**
Put in **m** and you have **men.**

Daddy got two men to make a pen.
The men put a bed in the pen.

Take the **b** away from **bed.**
Put in **f** and you have **fed.**
Put in l and you have **led.**

Then I led my pet into the pen.
I fed it and put it to bed.

Say these words: **pet, met, fed, led, pen, men.**

Two Ways to Make New Words

Ran is a word that you know.

Take the **r** away from **ran.**

Now you have a new word, **an.**

Here is a picture of an ostrich.

You know the word **mother.**

Take the **m** away from **mother.**

That will make a new word, **other.**

Penny plays with other little girls.

Take **c** away from **cold.**

Now you see a new word, **old.**

Where do you see an old mitten?

Take **t** away from **tears.**

That will make a new word, **ears.**

A rabbit has big ears.

What word will **look** and **ed** make?

look   **looked**   **look ed**

What word will **jump** and **ed** make?

jump   **jumped**

What word will **help** and **ed** make?

help   **helped**

Who helped Daddy?

Penny helped him.

What word will **thank** and **ed** make?

thank   **thanked**

Who thanked Dot for the airplane?

Janet thanked her for it.

What word will **fish** and **ed** make?

fish   **fished**

Tommy fished in the cold water.

Willie fished there, too.

One Color for Three

Penny Wants to Paint

"Daddy, may I help you paint?"
asked Penny.

"No, Penny," said her daddy.
"I will have to paint these things.
You may paint your toy horse
if you want to."

"I will," said Penny.
"I will paint it yellow."

98

"Look, Daddy," said Penny.
"See my yellow horse.
What can I paint now?
I still have some paint in the can."

"I do not know," said her daddy.
"You will have to find something."

"I know what I can paint,"
said Penny.
And away she went with her paint.

What Color Will It Be?

"No, no, Penny!" said Janet.
"That yellow paint
makes my house look bad."

"I like yellow," said Penny.
"It is a good color for a house.
Your house has to have some paint.
I will paint it for you.
It will look like a new house."

Up came Jack.

"Go on, Janet," said Jack.
"Let her paint the house."

"Not yellow!" said Janet.

"Maybe Daddy has some white paint,"
said Jack.
"That is a good color for a house.
We will see what colors Daddy has."

"Daddy, Janet wants to paint
her little house," said Jack.

"May we have some paint?"

"Which color?" asked Daddy.
"I have blue or yellow or white."

"I want yellow," said Penny.

"I choose blue," said Janet.

"I know what is a good color
for that little house," said Jack.
"White is just the color for it."

"The house will have to be yellow," said Penny.

"I have put yellow paint on it."

"Paint it white!" said Jack.
"White is a good color for it."

"It is my house," said Janet.
"I choose blue for it."

"But look here!" said Jack.
"There is too little yellow,
too little blue, and too little white."

103

No Stripes!

"I know!" said Jack.
And then he laughed.
"We will paint the house in stripes.
We can make the stripes go around
and around or up and down."

"Not on my house," said Janet.
"I do not want my house
to look like a zebra."
Then they all laughed.

"Do what you want to," said Daddy.
"Here are the paints you may have.
Some yellow paint for you, Penny.
Some blue paint for you, Janet.
And some white paint for Jack.
Now run away and let me paint."

"Come with me," said Jack.
"I know what we can do
with these paints."

Too Many Colors!

"Penny, you may have yellow," said Jack.

"Put your paint into this can. Janet, you may have blue. Put your paint in here, too. And I will have white."

"Will my house be yellow and blue and white?" asked Janet.

"That is too many colors. It will look funny."

"You will like this," said Jack.
"Look in the can now."

"Look at that color!" said Penny.
"It is not blue or yellow or white!"

"It is green!" said Janet.
"I like that color.
How did we get green paint?"

"Blue and yellow make green,"
said Jack.
"And with white it is still green."

Three Colors in One

"Janet, which color do you choose for your house now?" asked Jack.

"I choose green!" said Janet.

"So do I!" said Penny.

Then they all laughed because green was all they had.

Happy
Days

Here are:

Wait for Andy

Hurry Up, Andy!

One day Andy was out for a ride in his wagon.

Up ran Dick and Jack.

"Put away your wagon!" said Dick.
"We want you to go with us.
Hurry up, Andy.
Take your wagon home.
We will wait here for you."

112

"Where will we go?" asked Andy.

"To the circus parade," said Jack.
"We will have to hurry
or the parade will be gone.
Take your wagon home.
Get back here as fast as you can!"

"Wait for me," said Andy,
and away he went with his wagon.

Andy put away his wagon.
Soon the boys saw him coming back.
But he was not coming very fast.
The boys wanted him to hurry.

"Hurry up, Andy!" cried Jack.
"Hurry up, or we will never
get down to see the circus parade.
We want to get to First Street
before the parade has gone by."

"We can't wait," cried Dick.
"Hurry up!"

Off Comes a Shoe!

"Wait!" cried Andy.
"My shoe is coming off!"

"We can't wait!" said Jack.
"The circus parade will be gone!"

"Hurry up!" said Dick.
"We want to get to First Street
before the circus wagons go by!"

His shoe was about to come off,
but Andy began to run.

Then the shoe did come off.

There was Andy with one shoe off
and one shoe on.

"Wait for me!" he cried.

"My shoe has come off.

I can't run with one shoe off!"

Andy was so far behind the boys
that they did not hear him.

So they did not wait.

They were in a hurry to see
the circus wagons on First Street.

Andy sat down and put on his shoe.
Then he looked up the street
and down the street.

He was so far behind the boys
that he could not see them at all.
Andy was all alone.

"They did not wait for me," he said.
"I will have to go on alone.
I can't see the parade here."

Then Andy heard something.
It was far away,
but it was coming down his street.
What could it be?

Here Comes the Parade

Andy had heard the circus band.
Now the parade was not far off.
And there he stood all alone!

First came the big circus horses.
Behind them came the circus band.
The band was what Andy had heard.

Behind the band came a man
on a big elephant.

Andy stood there all alone
and looked up at the man.

The man looked down at Andy.

Then Andy heard the man say,
"Boy, do you want a ride?"

"Yes, I do!" said Andy.

Look at Andy Now!

"Up you go!" said the man.

And there Andy sat all alone
on the back of an elephant.
Soon the band began to play again.
The parade came to First Street.
And Andy went riding an elephant
down First Street in the parade!

It was fun to be riding all alone
on the back of an elephant.

Andy looked down — far down —
at the man with the elephant.

He looked down at the band.

It was riding in the band wagon.

He looked down at the boys and girls
who had come to see the parade.

Down there he saw Dick and Jack.
How far away they were!
He called down to them.

Dick and Jack looked up — far up —
and saw Andy riding an elephant.
He was riding behind the band
in the parade!

"Look at Andy!" called Dick.
"He is riding an elephant!
He is riding it all alone!"

"Look at Andy!" called Jack.
"He is riding behind the band!"

Andy heard all they said.
Riding an elephant was fun!

After the Parade

The parade went up Green Street.
Then it came down High Street.
Soon it was back on the street
where Andy began his ride.

"I have to get off here,"
Andy called down to the man.

"I will tell the elephant
to let you off," said the man.

The band and the horses had gone on.
The man and the elephant
were about to go on, too.

"Thank you for the ride," said Andy.
"Riding an elephant is fun."

"I like it too," said the man.
Then he went away with the elephant.

"I want to thank the elephant, too,"
Andy called to the man.

"I will tell him," the man called back.

The boys and girls wanted to hear
Andy tell about riding an elephant.

"Tell us all about it," said Dick.

"I can't tell you now," said Andy.
"My shoe is coming off."

"We will wait," said Dick.

Andy put on his shoe.
Then he did tell them
about riding alone on an elephant.

Who Wants to Run Away?

Circus Pictures

The circus was now far away,
but pictures of it were still around.

Day after day Andy looked at them.

"There is the picture of the elephant
I had a ride on," he said.

"Some day I am going to be
an elephant man in a circus.

When the circus comes again,
I am going away with it."

Then one day Dot saw Andy
going down the walk all alone.
He was in a big hurry.

"Where are you going?" Dot called.

"The circus is here," said Andy.
"I am going to run away.
I am going with the circus.
Do not tell Mother and Daddy."

"In those clothes?" asked Dot.
"Can't you get circus clothes?"

"Yes, I can," said Andy.
And back he went to get them.

In Circus Clothes

Soon Andy came down the walk again.
He had on his circus clothes,
and he had on new black shoes.

"You can't walk around the circus
in those new shoes," Dot said.
"You had better take time
to get shoes you can walk in.
Put those shoes in your wagon."

"I am in a hurry,
but I had better do that," said Andy.

And back he went again.

130

Down the walk Andy came again.
"I am going now," he said.

"Why don't you get Tip?" Dot asked.
"She can do tricks in the circus."

"I had better do that," said Andy.

"Why don't you take time to get
circus clothes for Tip, too?" asked Dot.

"I will," said Andy.
"Wait and see how she looks."

And off he went to get Tip.

A Circus Dog

"How about Tip now?" Andy asked.
"How do you like her clothes?"

"She looks like a circus dog now,"
said Dot.
"But what is the little pail for?"

"For my work," said Andy.
"I am going to water the elephants."

"Why don't you get a big pail
for that work?" asked Dot.

"Maybe I had better take time
to do that, too," said Andy.

"This big pail will be better
for my work," said Andy.

"What will you use for a bed
after your work is done?" asked Dot.

"You are going to work hard.
You will want a good bed
when you have done all that work.

Why don't you take something
to use for beds for you and Tip?

You had better take time to get
another wagon to put them in."

"I had better do that," said Andy.

Two Wagons Are Going

"That wagon is too big
for that little string," said Dot.

"Why don't you use a strong rope?
Strong rope is better for that work.
Go back and get a strong rope.
Get some clean clothes, too.
You will want some clean clothes
to put on after your work is done."

"I have all I can take," said Andy.
"I have shoes, and beds, and a pail."

But Andy went back for clean clothes
and a strong rope to use on the wagons.

Andy put his clean clothes
into the big wagon.

"Now I am done,
and I am going on!" he said.

"Wait, Andy," said Dot.
"Can't you get a good, strong broom?
You will have to clean the cages.
You had better have a good,
strong broom to use for that work.
Then you can get it done in a hurry."

"I will get a broom," said Andy.
"I know I will have to clean cages."

Wait for Cakes!

"Now I am going," said Andy.

"I have circus clothes, new shoes,
two beds, a pail, and clean clothes.

I have a strong broom to use
when I clean the cages."

"What about some cakes?" Dot asked.

"Mother just made some for us.

Can't you take time to stop
and eat some cakes?"

"I am in a big hurry,
but I will stop for cakes," Andy said.

Soon Dot came back with the cakes
that her mother had made.

She gave Andy a cake.

"These are better than anything
you will get in the circus," she said.

"Take time to eat one."

Andy did that and said,
"I like cake better than anything."

"Have another cake, Andy," Dot said.

"Mother made them for us.

You have to be strong
to clean cages and water elephants."

"Put one in my pocket," said Andy.

"I can't stop to eat another cake."

Andy Is Off

Down the walk Andy went.
The wagons were hard to pull.
Dot laughed to see him work so hard.

"He will stop and come back,"
she said to herself.
"He does not have much to eat.
He has no money.
He can't get anything to eat.
He will find out that home
is much better than the circus.
It will not be fun to clean cages."

But this time Andy did not stop.

The two wagons were hard to pull.
It made Andy hot to work so hard.
Soon he had to stop.

"We will stop here, Tip," he said.
"These wagons are hard to pull.
It is much too hot to work so hard.
We will stop and eat the cake.
I like cake better than anything."

Andy gave some cake to Tip.
Then he sat down.
"The cages can wait," he said.
Soon he went to sleep.

Get Up, Andy!

Andy heard somebody call,
"Get up, Andy! Get up!"

"Don't you know better than to sleep
all day?" he heard a man ask.

"How much work have you done?

Have you done anything at all?

Why don't you get your broom
and use it to clean those cages?"

"I can't clean the cages all alone!"
Andy said — and then he looked up.

There stood his daddy and Dot.

"How did you find me?" asked Andy.

"Tip came home alone," said Daddy.
"She made us come back with her."

"Do you want to go on?" Dot asked.
"It will be fun to clean cages."

"I want to go back," said Andy.
"It is too far to pull these wagons."

"Going back is much better than
going on to clean cages," said Daddy.

"Anything is better than that."
said Andy.

A Dog of Her Very Own

Dot Tells Her Wish

Dot wanted a little dog.

Day after day Bill heard her say,

"Bill, I wish I had a dog of my own."

Then Bill would say,
"I wish I had a dog of my own, too.
But what good does it do to wish?
You can't get a dog that way."

"I know it," Dot would say.
"But I still wish I had one."

One day Dot was out walking
with her daddy.

As they were walking along,
Dot saw a little black dog.

Dot said, "I wish I had
a little black dog like that one.

I would like one for my very own."

"I know you would," said her daddy.

"But it would take too much money
to get a dog like that."

Dot and her daddy went on.

As they were walking along, Dot said, "I have money of my own.

I could use that.

I wish we could go back.

I would ask the man how much he wants for that dog."

"You may go back if you wish," said Dot's daddy.

"I will wait for you here."

Away went Dot as fast as she could run.

Dot Wants More Money

Soon Dot came back.

Dot's daddy could see
that she was not happy at all.

She was walking along
with her head down.

"How much did he want?" said Daddy.

"Too much," said Dot.
"But I still wish I had that dog.
I want a little dog of my own.

"If I could get some more money,
I could get the dog."

146

Dot's daddy did not say anything about more money.

He just went walking along.

Then Dot said, "I still wish I could have that dog for my own."

"I know you do," said her daddy. "But it takes much more money than we can give for a dog now.

Maybe we can find some other dog which you would like."

"I wish we could," said Dot. "Can we look for one tomorrow?"

"Not tomorrow," said Dot's daddy.

"It would take more time
than I will have.

Tomorrow I have to go to the farm.

Would you like to go along?"

"Yes, I would," said Dot.

"I like to go to the farm.

Maybe we will see some dogs
on the way.

If we do, may I stop
and look at them, Daddy?"

"Not tomorrow," said her daddy.

"I have too much work to do."

"Then can we look for a dog
the day after tomorrow?" Dot asked.

"No, not then," said her daddy.

"We will do that some other time."

To the Farm

The next day Dot's mother asked, "Will you be walking to the farm?"

"Not this time," said Dot's daddy.

Dot said, "Walking will be fun when I have a little dog.
Maybe I will have him next time."

"Are you still wishing for a dog?" asked her daddy.
"Tomorrow you will make some other wish."

"Tomorrow I will still want a dog more than anything," said Dot.

On the way to the farm
the horse went fast.

Soon Dot said,
"Daddy, there is the big gate.
I like to play on that gate."

"It is more fun to play
on the other gate," said her daddy.

"What other gate?" asked Dot.

"The wishing gate," said her daddy.
"It is the gate to the next farm.
I will have time to show it to you
before I go to work."

The Wishing Gate

"There it is!" said Dot's daddy.

"Is that a gate?" asked Dot.

"It is a wishing gate," said Daddy. "Wishing gates are not like others. The next time we come out here maybe we will do some wishing."

"Daddy, if l make a wish here, will it come true?" asked Dot.

"Maybe — if you think it will," Daddy said as he went off to work.

151

As soon as her daddy had gone,
Dot got up on the wishing gate.

"I have never seen a wishing gate
before," she said to herself.

"How can it make wishes come true?
I don't think it can.
But what if it could!
It is not like other gates.
I think I will make one wish now.
Then the next time I come here
I will make some more wishes.

Maybe one of the wishes
will come true."

For a long time Dot sat very still.
She did not say a word.
Then she said to herself,
"I think I will make three wishes.
No, I think I had better
make one wish three times."

So she said to the wishing gate,
"I wish I had a little dog.
I wish I had a little black dog.
I wish I had a little black dog
just like the one I have seen.

"Wishing gate, I think that you
can make that little wish come true."

Dot stood up to look for her daddy.
Away off on the next farm
he was walking around at his work.
He had not seen or heard her
make her wish.
She ran to tell him about it.

"Daddy, have you ever made wishes
on the wishing gate?" Dot asked.

"Many, many times," he said.

"Have the wishes ever come true?"
she asked.

"I think some have," he said.

"Did it take long?" she said.
"Did a wish ever come true
the very next day?"

"It may have," said her daddy.
"Did you make some wishes?"

"I made just one wish," said Dot.
"Guess what I wished for."

"A long, blue pig," said her daddy.

"Have you ever seen one?" Dot asked.
"Guess again, Daddy."

"It would take too long to guess
all that you wished for," said Daddy.
"You had better tell me."

"I wished three times," said Dot.
"I wished for a dog.
I wished for a little dog.
I wished for a little black dog.
I think my wish will come true."

"You must not think too much
about the wishing gate," Daddy said.
"You don't think we will ever get
all we have wished for, do you?"

"I guess not," said Dot.
"But I think I will get my wish.
Maybe I will get it by tomorrow."

"I think it can't come true
by tomorrow," said her daddy.
"Some wishes take a long, long time.

"We must go along now.
You can come back and make
more wishes some other time."

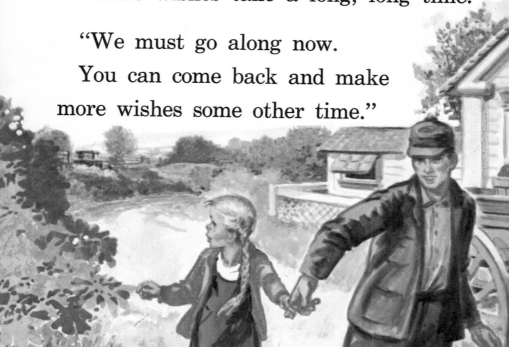

Is the Wish Coming True?

On the way home, Dot and her daddy
went along by the next farm.

A little dog came running out.

He ran along by the wagon.

"Look, Daddy!" cried Dot.

"A little dog is running after us."

"I think he will soon stop running
and go back to the house," said Daddy.

"He must belong on that farm."

"I guess he belongs
to some other little girl," said Dot.

But the little dog did not stop.
He kept on running behind the wagon.
Dot kept looking back.

"I don't think the little dog
belongs on that farm," said Dot.
"He is still running after us.
Can't we stop and take him in?"

"We had better not," said Daddy.
"He must belong around here.
Somebody may be looking for him.
You would not want to take him
away from some other little girl."

"No, I guess not," said Dot.

At first, the little dog kept
running along just behind the wagon.

But soon he was far behind.

Dot kept looking back as long as
the little black dog could be seen.

She kept on looking back
when just a black dot could be seen.

She kept on looking back
when he could not be seen at all.

"He looked just like the dog
I wished for," said Dot.

"But he must have gone back home.
I guess he belongs on that farm."

Still Dot kept on looking back.
She kept on looking for a long time
after she got out of the wagon.

"He got too far behind," she said.

"I guess he went back," said Daddy.
"He must belong on that farm."

Dot looked back again.
Away off she saw something.
It was just a little black dot!
Then it was a big black dot!

"Look, Daddy!" she cried out.
"Here comes the little black dog!"

Soon the little black dog
was at Dot's feet, looking up at her.

"Daddy, may I have him?" she asked.
"He came all the way home with us.
May I have him for my very own?"

"No, Dot," said her daddy.
"We must find out who owns him.
I think he belongs to the man
on the farm next to ours.
I have seen him over there.
I had better call up the man."

Dot's daddy went to call the man.
Dot sat down by the little dog.

"Where is your home?" she asked.
"Do you belong to some other girl?
Why were you running away?
Did you ever run away before?
Would you ever run away if I kept you
for my own little dog?
I wished for a dog just like you."

The little dog never said a word.
He sat there looking very happy.

Soon Dot's daddy came back.
He looked happy too.
He must have heard good news.

"The little dog belongs to a man
who must go away soon," said Daddy.
"He said you may have the dog."

"My very own little dog!" said Dot.
"You are just what I wished for.
Do you think that wishing gates
ever make wishes come true?
I guess I do."

"Woof!   Woof!" said the little dog.

Say the word **came.**
Take the **c** away from **came.**
Put in **g** and you have **game.**

I know a game that we can play.

Take the **g** away from **game.**
Put in **n** and you have **name.**

What is the name of the game?

Take the **n** away from **name.**
Put in **t** and you have **tame.**

The name of the game is
Tame the Elephants.

Take the **t** away from **tame.**
Put in **s** and you have **same.**

Will we play the same game tomorrow?

164

Say the word **choose.**
Hear the sound of **ch** in **choose.**

Put **ch** with **in.**
Now you have a new word, **chin.**

What has Penny on her chin?
She has ice cream on her chin.
Two chins would be too many chins.

Take **st** away from **stop.**
Put in **ch** and you have **chop.**

What did the man use to chop with?
What did he chop down?
Show how you chop.

Take **tr** away from **trick.**
Put in **ch** and you have **chick.**

Here is a little yellow chick.
What would a chick like to eat?
Where have you seen some chicks?

What word will **want** and **ed** make?

want   **wanted**

What did Janet want?

She wanted some paints.

Did she get what she wanted?

What word will **count** and **ed** make?

count   **counted**

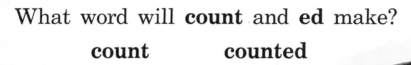

Janet counted the colors.

How many colors did she count?

Say the colors that she counted.

What word will **paint** and **ed** make?

paint   **painted**

Janet painted a picture.

It is the picture of a goat.

Do you think that the picture
she painted looks like a goat?

Pails and Pails of Paint

This House Will Not Do

Mrs. Blue had a little red house.
It was by the water.
She had two kittens and a calf.
She had a horse to pull her wagon.

When the house was new,
it was as red as red could be.
But now the paint was all coming off.

One day Mrs. Blue said to herself,
"I will have to find a new house.
This house will not do.
I don't like the way it looks.
The paint is coming off."

She put all of her things
into her wagon.
All but her broom.
She could not find her broom.

Mrs. Blue said to the kittens,
"You may ride in the wagon with me."
She said to the calf, "You walk
along behind the wagon."
She said to the horse,
"You are strong.
You can pull the wagon."

Will This House Do?

Away they all went to find
another house.

After they had gone a long way,
they came to a little yellow house.
"I like this house," said Mrs. Blue.
"No one is here.
We will stop here."

The next day Mrs. Blue
looked around.

"I like this little house," she said.
"Do you kittens like it here?"

"We like it," said the kittens.
"We like to sleep by a fire at night."

"The calf likes it here too,"
said Mrs. Blue.
"He can find good things to eat."

"Now I will get some water for you,"
she said to the horse.
"I will have to pull it up in a pail
with a strong rope."

"Here is some good cold water,"
said Mrs. Blue.

"I don't want water that you have
to pull up in a pail," said the horse.
"I don't want it at all."

Mrs. Blue put the pail of water down
and went into the house.
But the horse did not want the water.
He just stood there all day long.

"My! My!" said Mrs. Blue.
"Tomorrow we will see
what can be done.
It is too dark now."

The next day they went looking
for another house.

Soon they came to a green house.

"Do you like this house?"
Mrs. Blue asked the horse.

"Yes, I do," said the horse.
"The water looks good and you
will not have to pull it up in a pail."

"We like it here," called the kittens.
"We can sleep in a box by the fire."

"I don't like it here," said the calf.
"I don't see anything good to eat."

"That is too bad!"
Mrs. Blue said to the calf.
"I like the green house.
I do not want to go away.
But you must have
something good to eat.
I guess we had better go on."

Off they went to find another house.

Soon they saw a very little house.
"Maybe this house will do,"
Mrs. Blue said to herself.
"There is water for the horse and
something green for the calf to eat."

Mrs. Blue called, "Here, kittens!
Here is some cream for you."

The kittens did not come.
She looked around for them.
"There you are!" she said.
"Why are you behind the box?"

"We don't like this house,"
said one of the kittens.
"There is no fire to sleep by."

"This house will not do at all,"
Mrs. Blue said.
"You must have a fire to sleep by.
We will look for another house."

The Little White House

"Here is a little white house,"
said Mrs. Blue.

"I like this little house.

It looks new.

It is just the house for us.

There is water for the horse.

I will not have to pull it up
in a pail.

There is something good
for the calf to eat.

And a fire can be made
for the kittens to sleep by.

We will stop here."

A man came around the house.
He had a funny cap on his head.
He had big pockets in his clothes.
He had a pail of white paint.

"Is this your house?"
asked Mrs. Blue.

"No," said the man.
"It is not mine, but I have put
some white paint on it.
A man gave me pails and pails
of paint.
It was more paint than I could use
on my own house.
I did not have anything much to do.
So I put white paint on all the
houses around here.
It made them look like new."

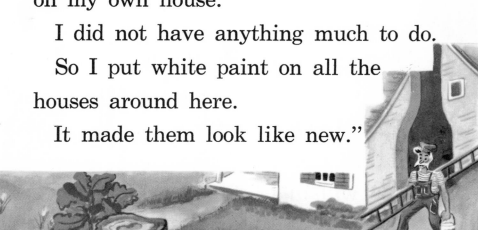

"You were very good to do that,"
said Mrs. Blue.

"We have looked and looked
for a house just like this.

May we go in and look around?"

"Yes, you may," said the man.
"Just walk in.

There is no one in the house.

I have a little more to paint.

Then I will be done.

It will not take long.

You will like this little house."

Mrs. Blue began to look around.

"Look here," she said.

"Here is a broom.

I have seen this broom before.

It looks just like my broom.

"How could my broom get here?

I did not take it with me.

I kept looking for it,

but I could not find it.

Let me think!

Now I know!"

"Mr. Man!" she called.
"What color was this house before
you put the white paint on it?"

"It was red," said the man.
"The paint was all coming off.
That is why I put white paint on it."

"My, my!" said Mrs. Blue.
"Do you know what we have done?
We have come back
to our own house.
It is good to be back home again."

Then she began to put
her things away.

Take the **g** away from **bag.**
Put in **d** and you have **bad.**
Take the **b** away from **bad.**
Put in **h** and you have **had.**
Take the **d** away from **had.**
Put in **t** and you have **hat.**

Janet had a new hat.
She put the hat in a bag.

Take the **h** away from **hat.**
Put in **c** and you have **cat.**

Soon the cat saw the bag.
Then the cat had the bag.
Janet said, "You bad cat!
Get away from my new hat!
Just for that you get no milk.
You are a bad cat!"

181

Take the **b** away from **box.**
Put in **f** and you have **fox.**
See the little red fox.

Take the **x** away from **fox.**
Put in **g** to make **fog.**
You can not see far in the fog.

Take the **f** away from **fog.**
Put in **l** and you make **log.**
Did you ever make a log house?

Take the **g** away from **log.**
Put in **t** and you have **lot.**
Take the **l** away from **lot.**
Put in **p** and you have **pot.**
Who got into a pot of paint?

Take the **t** away from **pot.**
Put in **p** and you have **pop.**
What made it go pop?

What word does **walk** and **ing** make?
walk   **walking**
Who is walking on the rope?

What word will **paint** and **ing** make?
paint   **painting**
The boy is painting his boat.

What word will **pull** and **ing** make?
pull   **pulling**
The goat is pulling the wagon.

What word will **hold** and **ing** make?
hold   **holding**
What is the elephant holding?

What word will **clean** and **ing** make?
clean   **cleaning**
Who is cleaning the walk?

cream

See, Say, and Hear

Look at **cream** and **cried**.
See the **cr** in those words.
Say **cream** and **cried**.
Did you hear the sound of **cr?**

Take the **b** away from **back**.
Put in **cr** and you have **crack**.
Hear the **cr** as you say **crack**.

Janet, there is a crack in my toy pig.
See what a big crack it is!

Take the **b** away from **by**.
Put in **cr** and you have **cry**.
Hear the **cr** as you say **cry**.

Don't cry, Penny, don't cry.
You may have this pig.
There is no crack in it.

184

trick

See the **tr** in **trick** and **true**.
Say **trick** and **true**.
Did you hear the sound of **tr?**

Take the **b** away from **by**.
Put in **tr** and you have **try**.
Hear the **tr** as you say **try**.

Try this, Janet.
You can do it if you try.

Take the **t** away from **tip**.
Put in **tr** and you see **trip**.
Hear the **tr** as you say **trip**.

Do you like to take a trip?
Where have you gone on a trip?

Take the **b** away from **back**.
Put in **tr** and you see **track**.
Hear the **tr** as you say **track**.

What runs on a track?

185

Hear the **f** in **fun** and **for**.
Put **f** with **at** to make **fat**.
Cream may make a kitten fat.

Take the **t** away from **fat**.
Put in **n** to make **fan**.
The fan belongs to Dot.

Take the **f** away from **fan**.
Put in **t** and you have **tan**.
What will give you a tan?

Take the **n** away from **tan**.
Put in **g** to make **tag**.
Do you like to play tag?

Take the **t** away from **tag**.
Put in **w** and you have **wag**.
What does a dog wag?

Take the **t** out of **but.**
Put in **n** to make **bun.**
Would you like a hot bun?

Take the **n** away from **bun.**
Put in **s** to make **bus.**
Do you ride on the bus?

Take the **b** away from **bus.**
Put in **pl** and you have **plus.**
Does two plus two make four?

Take the **s** away from **plus.**
Put in **m** to make **plum.**
Where did Jack find the plum?

Take the **pl** away from **plum.**
Put in **h** and you have **hum.**
What toy will hum?

One day Mrs. Kangaroo
saw Mr. Zebra running by her house.

"Why are you running?" she asked.

"I must find Mrs. Ostrich," he said.
"She is going to show me how to fly.
If I don't find her, I will never
know how to fly."

And Mr. Zebra began to cry.

"Don't cry," said Mrs. Kangaroo.
"Stop and think!
Did you ever see an ostrich fly?"

"No, I never did," said Mr. Zebra.
"I know an ostrich can't fly.
I had better not try flying.
I will go on walking and running."

And that is what he did.

VOCABULARY

UP AND AWAY is planned for use in the last half of the first year, following the primer, JACK AND JANET. Every one of the 151 words in the vocabulary of the primer is repeated in UP AND AWAY. The following list contains the 164 new words that are introduced in UP AND AWAY. The list does not include special words which are used in the lessons for developing phonetic power.

5. Willie	19. very	34. horse
6. cold	20. ——	white
wanted	21. ——	35. pig
7. fish	22. hiccups	were
Tommy	23. calf	36. ice
8. black	laughed	37. ——
yellow	24. if	38. ——
9. wet	stood	39. word
night	25. Mr.	40. ——
10. by	zebra	41. ——
fire	26. count	42. ——
11. dark	stripe	43. ——
feet	27. never	44. ——
12. somebody	three	45. ——
ran	28. Mrs.	46. ——
13. coming	ostrich	47. ——
still	29. sand	48. ——
14. sound	when	49. ——
jumped	30. happy	50. ——
15. around	kangaroo	51. ——
so	31. pocket	52. ——
16. ——	sat	53. ——
17. pulled	32. hot	54. ——
18. cried	day	
hard	33. because	
	tears	

55. boat
ride
56. five
Toosey
57. first
58. green
orange
59. before
cap
60. blue
violet
61. four
say
62. again
over
63. our
64. thing
65. began
66. ——
67. ——
68. ——
69. ——
70. ——
71. ——
72. paint
pencil
73. herself
74. color
picture
75. just
many

76. money
toy
77. some
78. maybe
79. party
prize
80. race
win
81. airplane
82. peanut
83. choose
84. bag
or
85. rope
86. cake
cream
87. which
88. ——
89. ——
90. ——
91. ——
92. ——
93. ——
94. ——
95. ——
96. ——
97. ——
98. ——
99. ——
100. ——

101. ——
102. ——
103. ——
104. ——
105. ——
106. ——
107. ——
108. ——
109. ——
110. ——
111. Andy
wait
112. hurry
wagon
113. circus
parade
114. can't
street
115. off
shoe
116. behind
far
117. alone
heard
118. band
119. elephant
man
120. an
riding
121. ——

122. called
123. ——
124. tell
125. ——
126. ——
127. ——
128. going
129. clothes
    walk
130. better
    time
131. don't
    why
132. pail
    work
133. done
    use
134. clean
    strong
135. broom
    cage
136. made
    stop
137. anything
    than
138. much
    pull
139. ——
140. ——
141. ——

142. own
    wish
143. would
144. along
    walking
145. Dot's
146. more
147. other
    tomorrow
148. farm
149. next
    wishing
150. gate
151. think
    true
152. seen
    wishes
153. long
154. ever
155. guess
    wished
156. must
157. belong
    running
158. kept
    looking
159. ——
160. ——
161. ——
162. ——

163. ——
164. ——
165. ——
166. ——
167. ——
168. ——
169. ——
170. ——
171. ——
172. ——
173. ——
174. ——
175. ——
176. ——
177. ——
178. ——
179. ——
180. ——
181. ——
182. ——
183. ——
184. ——
185. ——
186. ——
187. ——
188. ——

ACKNOWLEDGMENTS

Grateful acknowledgment is made to the following publishers and authors for permission to adapt and use copyrighted material:

To the Garden City Publishing Company, Inc., N.Y. for permission to adapt the story, *What About Willie?*, by Le Grand, copyright 1939.

To Alice D. Ransom for permission to adapt her story, "Robbie Rabbit and the Hiccups."

To Rand McNally and Company for permission to adapt the story, *Crybaby Calf*, written and illustrated by Helen and Alf Evers, copyright 1941.

To Mrs. Mabel G. La Rue for permission to adapt the story, "The Lucky Ducky," from the book, *The Tooseys*, published by Thomas Nelson and Sons.

To Marjorie Flack for permission to adapt *Wait for William* published by Houghton Mifflin Company, copyright 1935.

To Story Parade, Inc. for permission to adapt the story, "The Wishing Gate," by Phyllis Fenner.

To Abingdon-Cokesbury Press for permission to adapt the story, "*900 Buckets of Paint*," by Edna Becker, copyright 1949.

To H. Armstrong Roberts for permission to use the photographs reproduced on pages 3 and 53 of this book.

To the Monkmeyer Press Photo Service for permission to use the photograph reproduced on page 109 of this book.

Pictures by
Corinne Malvern
Charlot Bowman